GEORGE FR...

CONCERTO GROSSO

for Strings and Basso continuo
für Streicher und Basso continuo
B minor / h-Moll / Si mineur
Op. 6/12

Edited by/Herausgegeben von
Michael Nyman

Ernst Eulenburg Ltd

London · Mainz · Madrid · New York · Paris · Tokyo · Toronto · Zürich

G. F. HANDEL

Concerti Grossi, Op. 6

Handel's twelve Concerti Grossi, which came to be known as Op. 6, were written very quickly in late September and October 1739. On 29 October, the day before the last concerto to be composed was completed, Walsh announced in the *London Daily Post* that 'This Day are Publish'd, *Proposals* for Printing by Subscription, *Twelve Grand Concerto's* in Seven Parts, for four Violins, a Tenor, a Violoncello, with a Thorough-Bass for the Harpsichord. Compos'd by Mr. *Handel*.' This set of parts was published on 21 April 1740, after most or all of the concertos had been performed in Handel's winter concerts of 1739-40 as interval music in *Alexander's Feast, Acis and Galatea, L'Allegro, il Penseroso ed il Moderato*, and other choral works.

The earlier of these pre-publication performances may account for the additional oboe parts in Nos. 1, 2, 5 and 6, similar in function to those in the so-called 'Alexander's Feast' Concerto of 1736; it was perhaps to these concertos that Walsh referred when he re-advertized the subscription in the *London Daily Post* of 14 February 1740 and stated that 'Four of the above Concerto's have been perform'd at the Theatre-Royal in Lincoln's Inn Fields.' The internal evidence of Handel's autograph score shows that the oboe parts were added after the concertos had been completed, and possibly after the copy used for the printed parts had been prepared. The oboe parts were obviously written even more hastily than the rest of the score; no space had been allowed for them and various forms of shorthand were employed. Those movements originally written for Concerto No. 2 and later transferred to other concertos have no oboe parts, whereas the movements retained do, and this is further evidence that the oboes were an afterthought.

But had they been merely occasional, they would surely not have been included in the two 'presentation' volumes made under Handel's own or delegated supervision. One is part of the 'Granville' collection now in the British Museum, the other part of the 'Aylesford' collection previously owned by Sir Newman Flower but now publicly available in the Henry Watson Music Library, Manchester. The former has been dated 1744-5, but greater authority must be given to the Aylesford volume; it is closer to Handel's intentions and often reproduces exactly idiosyncracies in the autograph, as no other source does. Its probable origin was a non-extant copy made before some of the pages of Concerto No. 5 were mislaid. Each concerto is dated in this manuscript as they are in the autograph (except for No. 9), but not, as was previously thought, by Handel himself.

In view of the grandeur of the enterprise and Handel's evident supervision, the Walsh publication of the parts is surprisingly unreliable as a source; it must have been prepared in a hurry, judging both by the number of obvious errors and discrepancies of articulation between one instrument and another in identical passages, and by the inexplicable deviations from Handel's autograph. I have therefore consulted the sources in the following order of priority:

- *H* Handel's Autograph (British Museum R.M.20.g.11)
- *A* The 'Aylesford' score and parts (Manchester Public Library MS.130.4.v.85)
- *W* The Walsh published parts of 1740
- *G* The 'Granville' score (British Museum MS. Egerton 2944)

Solo and Tutti indications, though necessary in parts, are redundant in a score and have been omitted.

Dynamics that Handel wrote only above or below a whole system have been added to all the parts without comment in accordance with his obvious intention.

All sources have been used to complete patterns of articulation (slurs and staccato dots) begun or implied in the autograph, and these have been rationalized in parallel passages. Editorial additions have been indicated with square brackets or, in the case of slurs, with a stroke through the middle. Where staccato dots are found in one part and implied in others in the same bar, they have sometimes been added without comment. Nearly all dynamics, slurs and dots in the oboe parts are editorial, having been added because they appear in the corresponding violin parts.

Walsh's second edition of the parts (1741) differs from the first only in the figures that have been added to the concertino cello part. In the present edition these figures have been included only where the solo cello is playing independently of the bass.

The numbering of the movements is editorial.

Concerto No. 12 was completed on 20 October 1739, and was thus earlier than Nos. 9–11. It originally ended with an *Allegro moderato* in B major; a few days later Handel transferred this movement to No. 10 where it is in D major.

Michael Nyman, 1972

Editorial Notes

1. **Largo**

2, 3   All wedges ed., as also in 8 & 12 (cf. 1)

9   This *p* is the first dynamic in *A*, which has no *tr* in 10.

2. **Allegro**

1ff   No slurs in *A*

12–14   All wedges ed., except for Vc. & Basso in 13

14   Vl. II/Vla., 5: *H* untidy; Vla., 5 should perhaps be E sharp

20   Vl. I rip.: slur in *H* only; no source has slur in Vl. I conc.

31–3   All wedges ed., except Vc. & Basso; as also in 62

38   Vc. conc., 2–3: high C sharp in *H*, but Handel must have meant A.

44   Vl. II 2: C sharp in *H* is contradicted by figures under Basso, and has been changed to B.

48   Vl. II conc., 6–8: dots ed.

3. **Aria: Larghetto e piano**

H has this movement on three staves with Vl. III playing the Vla. stave.

39   All figures under Basso from here to end ed.

4. **Largo**

1   Vl. I conc.: dots ed. *A* has no slurs in this movement.

5. **Allegro**

The Fugue subject is from an organ piece by Zachow, Handel's teacher.

64   Vla. & Vc.: wedges ed.

G. F. HÄNDEL
Concerti Grossi, Op. 6

Händels 12 Concerti Grossi, die später als Op. 6 bekannt geworden sind, entstanden in rascher Folge gegen Ende September und im Oktober des Jahres 1739. Am 29. Oktober, am Tage vor der Vollendung des letzten Konzerts dieser Reihe, setzte Walsh die folgende Anzeige in die *London Daily Post:* ,,This day are Publish'd, *Proposals* for Printing by Subscription, *Twelve Grand Concerto's* in Seven Parts, for four Violins, a Tenor, a Violoncello, with a Thorough-Bass for the Harpsichord. Compos'd by Mr. Handel." (Hiermit erscheint heute die Subskriptionsanzeige für die Drucklegung von 12 grossen Konzerten für sieben Stimmen: vier Geigen, eine Bratsche, ein Cello und ein bezifferter Bass für das Cembalo). Diese Stimmen wurden am 21. April 1740 veröffentlicht, nachdem die meisten, oder sogar alle Concerti in Händels Winterkonzerten der Saison 1739-40 als Zwischenaktmusiken in *Alexander's Feast, Acis and Galatea, L'Allegro, il Penseroso ed il Moderato* und anderen Werken zur Aufführung gekommen waren.

Die früheren dieser Aufführungen, die vor der Drucklegung zustande kamen, mögen der Grund dafür gewesen sein, dass die Konzerte Nr. 1, 2, 5 und 6 zusätzliche Oboenstimmen enthalten, denn diese Konzerte erfüllten einen ähnlichen Zweck wie das sogenannte ,,Alexander's Feast Concerto" aus dem Jahre 1736. In der wiederholten Subskriptionsanzeige, die Walsh am 14. Februar 1740 in die *London Daily Post* setzte, und in der es hiess, dass ,,vier der obengenannten Konzerte im Theatre-Royal in Lincoln's Inn Fields aufgeführt" worden waren, hat es sich vielleicht um diese Konzerte gehandelt. Aus der Partitur von Händels Originalmanuskript ergibt sich, dass die Oboenstimmen nach der Vollendung der Konzerte, möglicherweise sogar erst nach der Fertigstellung des Exemplars, das als Vorlage für den Druck diente, hinzugefügt worden sind. Offensichtlich sind die Oboenstimmen in noch grösserer Eile geschrieben worden als der Rest der Partitur. Es war kein Platz für sie vorgesehen, und sie wurden in verschiedenen Arten von Kurzschrift notiert. Die Sätze, die ursprünglich für das Konzert Nr. 2 gedacht und später auf andere Konzerte übertragen worden sind, haben keine Oboenstimmen, während die Sätze, die in diesem Konzert verblieben sind, Oboen enthalten. Das ist ein weiterer Beweis dafür, dass die Oboen nachträglich hinzugefügt worden sind.

Wenn diese Stimmen nur für gelegentliche Zwecke gedacht gewesen wären, so wären sie bestimmt nicht in den beiden ,,Widmungsexemplaren", die unter Händels eigener oder bevollmächtigter Aufsicht hergestellt worden sind, enthalten. Einer dieser Bände ist ein Teil der ,,Granville"-Sammlung, die sich zur Zeit im British Museum befindet. Der andere ist in der ,,Aylesford"-Sammlung, die früher Sir Newman Flower gehört hat, zu der aber die Öffentlichkeit jetzt in der Henry Watson-Sammlung der Musikbibliothek in Manchester Zutritt hat. Der erstere ist 1744-5 datiert, aber der Band in der Aylesford-Sammlung muss als der zuverlässigere angesehen werden, weil er sich mehr an Händels Absichten hält, und weil er wiederholt gewisse Eigenheiten des Originalmanuskripts genauer wiedergibt als jede andere Quelle. Ihm lag wahrscheinlich eine verschollene Kopie zugrunde, die geschrieben wurde, bevor einige Seiten des Konzerts Nr. 5 verlorengingen. Jedes der Konzerte in diesem Manuskript, wie auch im Autograph (mit Ausnahme von Nr. 9) ist datiert, jedoch nicht, wie früher angenommen wurde, von Händel selbst.

Wenn man bedenkt, wie grossartig die Unternehmung geplant war, und dass sie offensichtlich unter Händels eigener Aufsicht stand, so erweisen sich die von Walsh herausgegebenen Stimmen als eine überraschend unzuverlässige Quelle. Aus der Zahl augenscheinlicher Druckfehler und den Uneinheitlichkeiten in der Zeichensetzung für verschiedene Instrumente in identischen Passagen, sowie aus den unerklärlichen Abweichungen von Händels Autograph, ergibt sich, dass diese Ausgabe mit Hast fertiggetellt worden ist. Aus diesem Grunde habe ich die Quellen nach ihrer Zuverlässigkeit geordnet und sie in dieser Reihenfolge zu Rate gezogen:

H Händels Autograph (British Museum R.M.20.g.11)

A Die „Aylesford"-Partitur und -Stimmen (Manchester Public Library MS.130.4.v.85)

W Die von Walsh 1740 veröffentlichten Stimmen

G Die „Granville"-Partitur (British Museum MS. Egerton 2944)

Die Bezeichnungen Solo und Tutti, die in den Stimmen ihren Sinn haben aber sich in der Partitur erübrigen, sind weggelassen worden. Dynamische Hinweise, die Händel nur über oder unter eine ganze Reihe von Liniensystemen gesetzt hat, sind, seiner offensichtlichen Absicht gemäss, allen Stimmen ohne weitere Erläuterung hinzugefügt worden.

Alle Quellen sind zu Rate gezogen worden, um die die Phrasierung betreffende Hinweise (Bindebögen, Staccatopunkte), die in der Originalpartitur angedeutet wurden oder sinngemäss erscheinen, zu vervollständigen, und diese Zeichen sind auch in den Parallelpassagen dementsprechend vereinheitlicht worden. Zusätze des Herausgebers erscheinen in eckigen Klammern oder, wie bei den Bindebögen, mit einem Strich durch die Mitte. Dort, wo Staccatopunkte in einer Stimme zu finden sind und sich in einer anderen von selbst verstehen, wird sie ohne Kommentar hinzugefügt worden. Fast alle dynamischen Hinweise, Bindebögen und Punkte in den Oboenstimmen sind vom Herausgeber hinzugefügt worden, um sie mit den entsprechenden Geigenstimmen in Einklang zu bringen.

Walshs zweite Ausgabe der Stimmen (1741) weicht nur darin von der Erstausgabe ab, dass die Cellostimme des Concertinos mit einer Bezifferung versehen ist. In der vorliegenden Ausgabe ist diese Bezifferung nur dort angegeben, wo das Cello eine vom Bass unabhängige Stimme hat.

Die Nummerierung der Sätze stammt vom Herausgeber.

Das Konzert Nr. 12 ist am 20. Oktober 1739 vollendet worden und wurde daher früher als die Konzerte Nr. 9–11 geschrieben. Ursprünglich endete es mit einem *Allegro moderato* in H-Dur. Ein paar Tage später übertrug Händel diesen Satz auf das Konzert Nr. 10, in dem er in D-Dur erscheint.

Michael Nyman, 1972

Deutsche Übersetzung Stefan de Haan

Concerto Grosso No. 12

4

2. Allegro

E. E. 6619

8

12

14

E.E. 6619

18

3. Aria: Larghetto e piano

4. Largo

5. Allegro